SCHOOLS LIBRARY SERVICE

D0306489

EAST SUSSEX SCHOOLS LIBRARY SERVICE	
10-Jun-2009	PETERS
1241503	

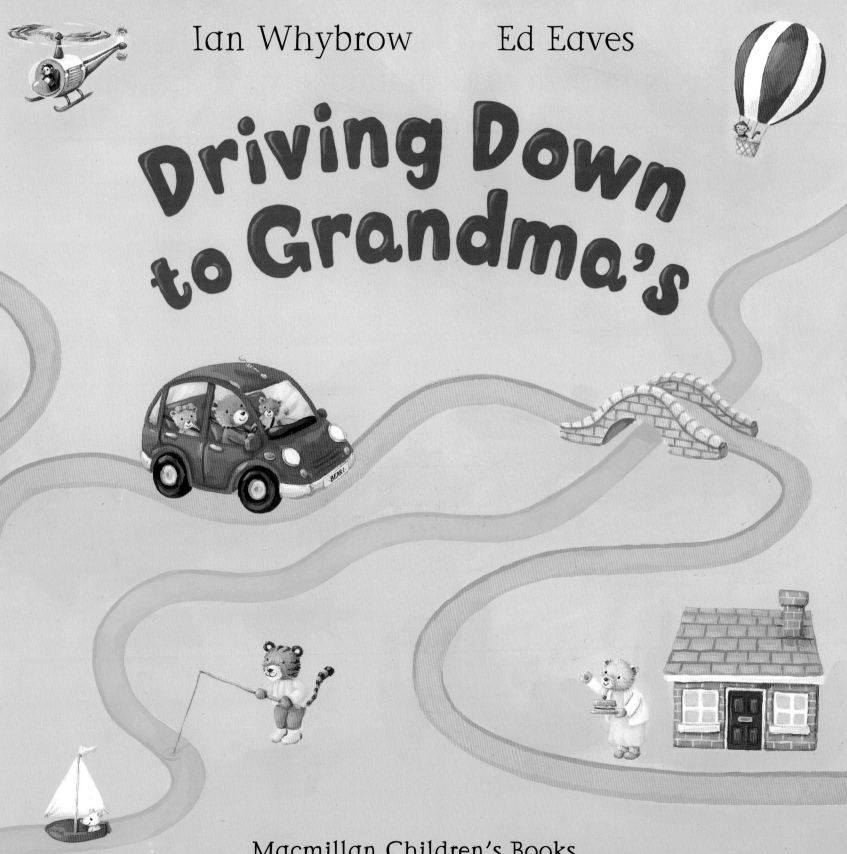

Ian Whybrow   Ed Eaves

Driving Down to Grandma's

Macmillan Children's Books

Driving down to Grandma's
With our mum.

Off we go with a

BRRUMM
BRRUMM
BRRUMM!

Here comes a fire engine!
What does it say?

"NEE NOR, NEE NOR,
Mind out of the way!"

Traffic jam! Music time!
Sing along with us!
Are you ready? Here we go –

Now we're at the petrol station!
Find a petrol pump.

Mum slams the door
And the door goes THUMP!

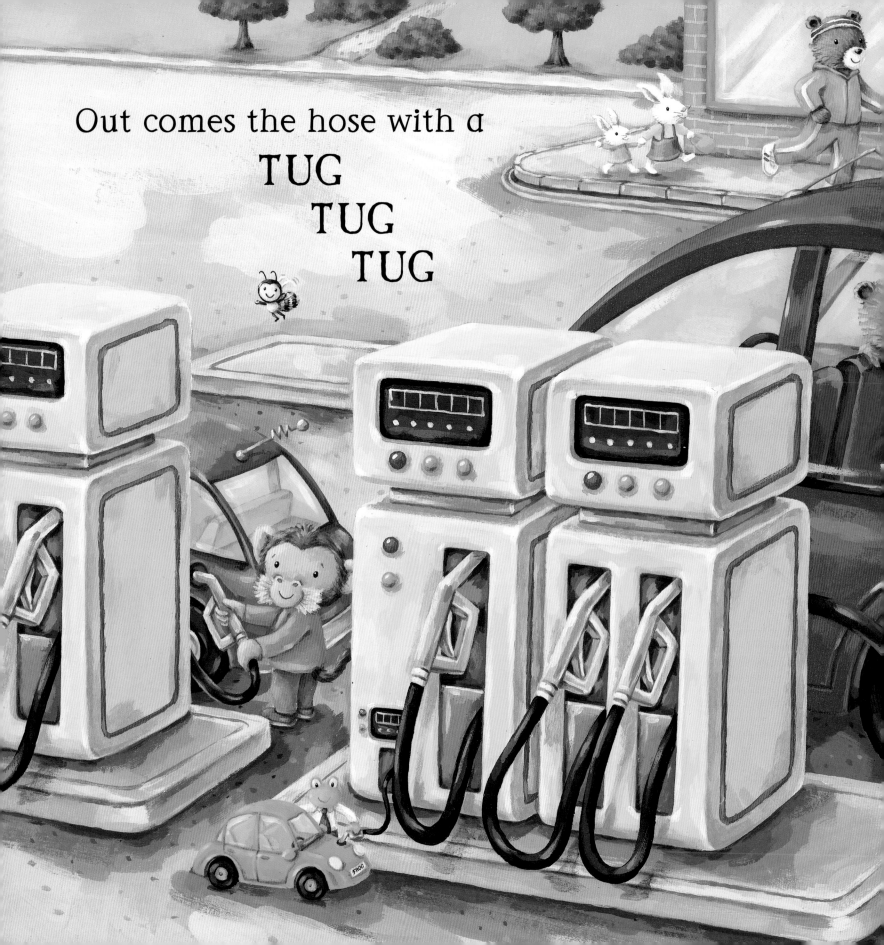

Out comes the hose with a
TUG
TUG
TUG

In goes the petrol –
GLUG
GLUG
GLUG!

Sitting in the carwash
Feeling like a fish.
Down comes the water –

Off we go again
With a **BUMP**
and a **CLONK**.

"Watch out, hedgehogs!"

HONK
HONK
HONK!

"Hello, Grandpa!"
"We've come for a chat!"
Knock on the door for Grandma –

RAT-A-TAT-TAT!

Grandma says, "How lovely!
I'm really glad you've come.
Is anybody hungry?"

"YUM YUM YUM!"

For Lucy Bowden & Brooke Noble – I.W.

For Granny – E.E.

First published 2009 by Macmillan Children's Books
a division of Macmillan Publishers Limited
20 New Wharf Road, London N1 9RR
Basingstoke and Oxford
Associated companies throughout the world
www.panmacmillan.com

ISBN: 978-0-230-01532-6 (HB)
ISBN: 978-0-230-70545-6 (PB)

Text copyright © Ian Whybrow 2009
Illustrations copyright © Ed Eaves 2009
Moral rights asserted.

All rights reserved. No part of this publication may be reproduced, stored in or introduced into a retrieval system,
or transmitted in any form, or by any means (electronic, mechanical, photocopying, recording or otherwise)
without the prior written permission of the publisher. Any person who does any unauthorized act in relation
to this publication may be liable to criminal prosecution and civil claims for damages.

1 3 5 7 9 8 6 4 2

A CIP catalogue record for this book is available from the British Library.

Printed in Belgium